Kelly Moss

Illustrated by Jim Keserich

Palmary Press

Published by Palmary Press
PO Box 778000
Henderson, NV 89077
702-272-0541
office@thesantaclub.net
www.thesantaclub.net

BookStudio

Publishing Consulting by BookStudio
www.bookstudiobooks.com

Illustrations by Jim Keserich
Book design by Lydia D'moch
Jacket and case design by Monkey C Media
Printed by Everbest Printing Co., Nansha, China
Production Date: April 1, 2011
Batch #: 99453
Published in the United States of America
ISBN 13: 978-0-9821340-1-6

9   8   7   6   5   4   3

17   16   15   14   13   12   11   10

www.thesantaclub.net

"It is more blessed
to give than to receive."
—Acts 20:35

To receive this book, you have to ask either one of two very important questions. Only those children who ask these questions get this book, because it is very special and somewhat secret.

If you have ever wondered about any of the questions on the next page and you really want the answer, then you must promise two things:

1. That you will not read the rest of this book without a parent or a guardian.

2. That you will not tell another child about this book or the answer to the questions on the next page unless your parent or guardian says it is ok. If you are ready, then look on the next page.

Is there a Santa Claus?
Is Santa Claus real?

The answer is . . .

Yes!

Yes, there is a Santa Claus! To tell the truth, there are millions of Santa Clauses all over the world.

Some are parents.

Some are grandparents.

And some
are people
who just
love to give.

All of these Santas
belong to a special club.
It is a club so special
that until recently
they didn't even know
that they belonged.
They all belong
to a club called ...

**OFFICIAL CLUB OF ALL SANTAS,
SMALL AND BIG, YOUNG AND OLD,
ALL OVER THE WORLD**

There are millions of members,
and the only way to get into the club
is to ask one of these questions:

Is there a Santa Claus?
Is Santa Claus real?

Only when a child is big enough to ask those questions does a child get into the club. Not all children are ready to join. Some are afraid to ask, some believe and do not have to ask. Others are just not old enough. But you are old enough because you asked the question.

Congratulations and welcome to the club!

All over the world
and for many, many years,
people have been giving gifts as Santa Claus.
The first Santa Claus was St. Nicholas.
He was very kind and jolly and looked a little
like the Santa with the red suit.

St. Nicholas was a follower
of a man named Jesus Christ.
He believed that Jesus
was the Son of God.

Jesus was born a very long time ago. He was so special that today many people go to church to learn more about him. Every day people read about Jesus's life in a book called the Bible. A whole part of the Bible is just about Jesus and his life. It is called the New Testament.

God loves Jesus very much. God also loves us, so he let Jesus come to be with us on earth. God gave us the gift of Jesus.

Jesus then gave us a very special gift, the gift of himself. He loved us so much that he ended up dying on a cross to help us. After Jesus died he came back to tell everyone that he was ok and he was going to Heaven to be with God. He is so special that we give gifts on his birthday. Do you know what day that is? It is Christmas!

Do You Like Christmas?

Christmas is when all the members of The Santa Club give gifts to children and people who need help. Also, it is Jesus's Birthday!

Happy Birthday Jesus!

God loves us, and gave us
the gift of Jesus.

Jesus loves us, and gave us
the gift of giving.

Because of this, St. Nicholas
gave gifts, too.

St. Nicholas gave gifts secretly
to children and families who were poor.
After he died many people became
a secret Santa just like St. Nicholas.
That is when The Santa Club was started.
For many years, millions of people
have been part of this very special club.

Today, members of

give gifts as Santa Claus,
just like the members before them.
These Santa Clauses love children
and other people so much that
they give gifts without getting
anything in return.